rockschool®

Male Vocals
Grade 8

Performance pieces, technical exercises and in-depth guidance
for Rockschool examinations

Acknowledgements

Published by Rockschool Ltd. © 2014 under license from Music Sales Ltd.
Catalogue Number RSK091416
ISBN: 978-1-908920-66-9

AUDIO
Backing tracks produced by Music Sales Limited
Supporting test backing tracks recorded by Jon Musgrave, Jon Bishop and Duncan Jordan
Supporting test vocals recorded by Duncan Jordan
Supporting tests mixed at Langlei Studios by Duncan Jordan
Mastered by Duncan Jordan

MUSICIANS
Neal Andrews, Lucie Burns (Lazy Hammock), Jodie Davies,Tenisha Edwards, Noam Lederman,
Beth Loates-Taylor, Dave Marks, Salena Mastroianni, Paul Miro, Ryan Moore, Jon Musgrave,
Chris Smart, Ross Stanley, T-Jay, Stacy Taylor, Daniel Walker

PUBLISHING
Compiled and edited by James Uings, Simon Troup, Stephen Lawson and Stuart Slater
Internal design and layout by Simon and Jennie Troup, Digital Music Art
Cover designed by Philip Millard, Philip Millard Design
Fact Files written by Stephen Lawson, Owen Bailey and Michael Leonard
Additional proofing by Chris Bird, Ronan Macdonald, Jonathan Preiss and Becky Baldwin
Cover photography © Startraks Photo / Rex Features
Full transcriptions by Music Sales Ltd.

SYLLABUS
Vocal specialists: Martin Hibbert and Eva Brandt
Additional Consultation: Emily Nash, Stuart Slater and Sarah Page
Supporting Tests Composition: Martin Hibbert, James Uings, Jon Musgrave, Jodie Davies,
Ryan Moore, Chris Hawkins, Jonathan Preiss

PRINTING
Printed and bound in the United Kingdom by Caligraving Ltd.
Media hosting by Dropcards

DISTRIBUTION
Exclusive Distributors: Music Sales Ltd.

CONTACTING ROCKSCHOOL
www.rockschool.co.uk
Telephone: +44 (0)845 460 4747
Fax: +44 (0)845 460 1960

Table of Contents

Introductions & Information

Page

Rockschool Grade Pieces

Page

Technical Exercises

Page

Supporting Tests

Page

Additional Information

Page

Welcome to Rockschool Male Vocals Grade 8

Welcome to the Rockschool Female Vocals Grade 8 pack. This book and accompanying download card contain everything you need to sing at this grade.

Vocals Exams

At each grade you have the option of taking one of two different types of examination:

- **Grade Exam:** a Grade Exam is a mixture of music performances, technical work and tests. You prepare three pieces (two of which may be Free Choice Pieces) and the contents of the Technical Exercise section. This accounts for 75% of the exam marks. The other 25% consists of: a Quick Study Piece (10%), two Ear Tests (10%), and finally you will be asked five General Musicianship Questions (5%). The pass mark is 60%.

- **Performance Certificate:** in a Performance Certificate you sing five pieces. Up to three of these can be Free Choice Pieces. Each song is marked out of 20 and the pass mark is 60%.

Book Contents

The book is divided into a number of sections. These are:

- **Exam Pieces:** in this book you will find six well-known pieces of Grade 8 standard. Each song is preceded by a Fact File detailing information about the original recording, the artist who sang on it and some recommended listening if you wish to research the artist further.

- **Piano and guitar notation:** every exam piece is printed with a piano part and guitar chords. Both are a representation of the overall band arrangement. These have been included to assist you with your practice should you wish to use a piano and/or guitar for accompaniment. In your exam you must perform to the backing tracks provided.

- **Vocal score:** in addition to the piano/vocal/guitar arrangement there is also a separate vocal-only score to allow you to view the vocal part on a single sheet of paper.

- **Technical Exercises:** there are a range of technical exercises in this grade. Some are notated in full, and some give a range of starting notes.

- **Supporting Tests and General Musicianship Questions:** in Vocals Grade 8 there are three supporting tests – a Quick Study Piece, two Ear Tests and a set of General Musicianship Questions (GMQs) asked at the end of each exam. Examples of the types of tests likely to appear in the exam are printed in this book.

- **General Information:** finally, you will find information on exam procedures, including online examination entry, marking schemes, information on Free Choice Pieces and improvisation requirements for each grade.

Audio

Each song in Vocals Grade 8 has an audio track that can be downloaded via the download card that comes with the book. This is a backing track with the vocal taken off so you can sing along with the band. The backing tracks should be used in examinations. There are also audio examples of the supporting tests printed in the book.

The audio files are supplied in MP3 format, the most widely compatible audio format in common usage – MP3s will likely be familiar to anyone with a computer, iPod, smartphone or similar device. Once downloaded you will be able to play them on any compatible device; we hope that you find this extra versatility useful.

Download cards

Download cards are easy to use – simply go to *www.dropcards.com/rsvocals* and type in the code on the back of your card. It's best to do this somewhere with a good connection, to ensure that the download is uninterrupted. If you have any problems with your download, you should be able to resolve them at *www.dropcards.com/help*.

Supporting Test Notation

The supporting tests in this book and its corresponding exam are written one octave higher than they sound. This is common practice and avoids excessive use of ledger notes.

We hope you enjoy using this book. You can find further details about Rockschool's Vocals and other instrumental syllabuses on our website: *www.rockschool.co.uk.*

SONG TITLE: A SONG FOR YOU
ALBUM: MY WORLD
RELEASED: 1993
LABEL: WARNER BROS.
GENRE: SOUL

PERSONNEL: RAY CHARLES (VOX+PIANO)

UK CHART PEAK: N/A
US CHART PEAK: N/A

BACKGROUND INFO

'A Song For You' was Ray Charles's 1993 cover of Leon Russell's tender 1970 ballad, which Elton John described as "an American classic". It featured on Ray Charles's album *My World*.

THE BIGGER PICTURE

Ray Charles Robinson was born in Georgia in 1930, and lost his sight aged seven due to glaucoma. At a school for the deaf and blind in St Augustine, Florida he learned to play piano, sax, trumpet and clarinet. By the age of 15, he was touring in the south, and when he moved to Seattle, his first recordings followed. Stylistically indebted to his idol, Nat 'King' Cole, he played on (and arranged) Guitar Slim's 12-bar blues hit 'The Things That I Used To Do' and soon had a breakthrough of his own with the song 'I Got A Woman' in 1955. A string of hits followed, including 'What'd I Say' and 'Hit The Road, Jack', and Charles's combination of gospel with blues and jazz coalesced into a sonic brew that became soul. The Father Of Soul didn't rest on his laurels. He had hits in the big band style, and brought his talents to the country and western genre in the 1960s. He re-emerged in the 1990s, and died of liver failure in 2004. A major biopic, *Ray*, was released that year.

NOTES

Charles was 62 when he recorded the 1993 album *My World*, an attempt to update his sound by including programmed rhythms and influences in vogue at the time. It was praised for Charles's ability to put his indelible stamp on the songs of other artists. When interviewed in *Entertainment Magazine* in 1993, he summed it up by saying: "The best way to understand what I do is to think of an actor. You get a script, you read it and then you ask yourself if you can fit into that script. 'Can I become that character?' That's what I do with my songs. When I think about doing a song, the first thing I deal with is the lyrics: are they making any sense to me, can I put myself into this?" Leon Russell's 'A Song For You' finds Charles in classic mood on vocal and keys, backed by a dynamic orchestral arrangement. "'A Song For You' has that line about: 'Living my life on stages, with 10,000 people watching'," he said. "You could tell that fella had been there."

RECOMMENDED LISTENING

Ray performs the song together with its author, Leon Russell, and Willie Nelson on the live DVD *Willie Nelson & Friends: Live And Kickin'*. *The Very Best Of Ray Charles* is also recommended.

A Song For You

Ray Charles

Words & Music by Leon Russell

SONG TITLE: APOLOGIZE
ALBUM: DREAMING OUT LOUD
RELEASED: 2006
LABEL: INTERSCOPE
GENRE: POP

PERSONNEL: RYAN TEDDER (VOX+KEYS)
ZACH FILKINS (GTR+VIOLA)
DREW BROWN (VARIOUS)
EDDIE FISHER (DRUMS)
BRENT KUTZLE (CELLO)

UK CHART PEAK: 3
US CHART PEAK: 2

BACKGROUND INFO

'Apologize' was the debut single from OneRepublic. Thanks to a remix by Timbaland – not to mention the songwriting skills of frontman Ryan Tedder – it became a monster hit in 2007.

THE BIGGER PICTURE

OneRepublic formed in Los Angeles circa 2003, after frontman Ryan Tedder persuaded his former school bandmate Zach Filkins to join him in LA. Tedder had worked in the music industry since college, first as an intern at Dreamworks Records, then as an apprentice to R'n'B producer Timbaland, who also helped Tedder with his own development as a music artist. OneRepublic – "a rock band that has an obsession with pop melodies", according to Tedder – were signed to Columbia Records and spent two and a half years working on their debut album. However, just months before the record's scheduled release date, the band were dropped by their label. Fortunately, OneRepublic were gaining fans on MySpace. "We blew up out of nowhere," said Tedder. OneRepublic were hot property and offers from record companies flooded in. In the end, the band decided to sign with a subsidiary of Interscope, represented by Tedder's former employer Timbaland.

NOTES

By the time OneRepublic signed their deal with Interscope, the band's debut album was already written, including a sparse ballad called 'Apologize'. Ryan Tedder told DigitalSpy: "Timbaland then re-mixed the song and told us that he thought the song was a hit with or without him. But then he said, 'If you let me put this song on my album, it will speed the process up…'" But OneRepublic were wary, concerned that a remix would give people the wrong impression of the band. "We're not hard rock but we are a rock band," Tedder said, "So to have our song remixed and made so much more pop, we were very reluctant. But then we were like, 'If this opens the door and allows more people to hear our album, it gives us the opportunity to let them hear our other songs. I think we can win them over.'" And win them over they did; 'Apologize' was an international success, and in America it ranked as the biggest radio airplay hit in the history of Billboard's weekly airplay chart.

RECOMMENDED LISTENING

OneRepublic's debut album, *Dreaming Out Loud*, may have had a troubled launch, but it stands as the best testimony to the band's abilities.

Apologize

OneRepublic

Words & Music by Ryan Tedder

1. I'm

Oh._____

2. I'd

It's

SONG TITLE: GRACE

ALBUM: GRACE

RELEASED: 1994

LABEL: COLUMBIA

GENRE: ALT. ROCK

PERSONNEL: JEFF BUCKLEY (VOX+GTR)

GARY LUCAS (GTR)

MICK GRØNDAHL (BASS)

MATT JOHNSON (DRUMS)

UK CHART PEAK: N/A

US CHART PEAK: N/A

BACKGROUND INFO

'Grace' was the title track of Jeff Buckley's only studio album released in his lifetime, *Grace*.

THE BIGGER PICTURE

Jeffrey Scott Buckley (1966–1997) was one of the most critically-acclaimed singers of the 1990s. He was the son of 1960s–1970s folk/jazz artist Tim Buckley, but the two met only once, when Jeff was eight years old. Buckley's mother is a classically-trained pianist and cellist, and Buckley decided to pursue a career in music aged 12. He started playing a guitar he found in his grandmother's closet and played in his school jazz band. As an early teen, he listened to a lot of progressive/heavy rock such as Rush, Genesis, Yes and Led Zeppelin. Buckley attended LA's Musicians Institute and completed a one-year course at 19. He sometimes seemed ambivalent about music school. Buckley once told *Rolling Stone* it was "the biggest waste of time", but later noted he appreciated studying music theory, saying, "I was attracted to really interesting harmonies, stuff that I would hear in Ravel, Ellington, Bartók…" *Grace* was the only studio album he completed. Buckley drowned in 1997 while working on his second album, subsequently released as *Sketches For My Sweetheart The Drunk*.

NOTES

The song 'Grace' originated from Buckley's time playing in New York City in 1991. The song was based on an instrumental called 'Rise Up To Be', written by Buckley's then-collaborator, guitarist Gary Lucas. Lucas was 20 years Buckley's senior and a veteran of Captain Beefheart's band, but the two worked together under the name Gods And Monsters. Buckley developed the song but Lucas has a co-writer credit, as he does for *Grace*'s opener, 'Mojo Pin'. Buckley's lyrics were inspired by his saying goodbye to his then-girlfriend at the airport on a rainy day. In his spoken intro on the *Live At Sin-é* EP, Buckley says, "It's about not feeling so bad about your own mortality when you have true love." Buckley's leaping and vibrato'd vocals were a trademark – he could literally go from whisper to scream in a single song. Buckley cited vocal inspirations as diverse as Led Zeppelin's Robert Plant, Nusrat Fateh Ali Khan, Morrissey, Billie Holiday and Robert Johnson.

RECOMMENDED LISTENING

Start with *Grace*, full of remarkable singing. For contrasting Buckley vocals, listen to his gently soulful falsetto on 'Everybody Here Wants You' and 'Opened Once' from *Sketches…*

Grace

Jeff Buckley
Words & Music by Jeff Buckley & Gary Lucas

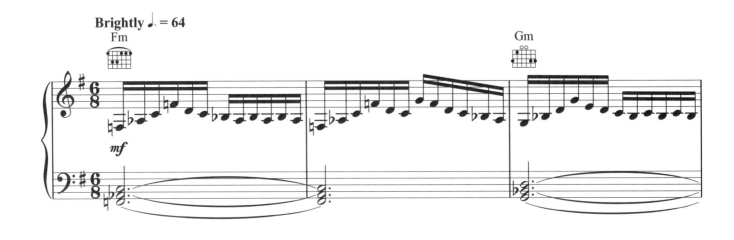

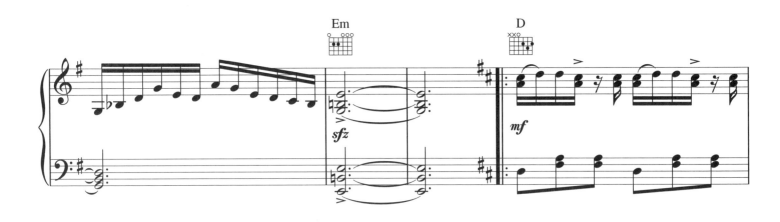

1. There's the moon ask-ing to stay
2. And she weeps on my arm,
3. And I feel them drown my name, so

SONG TITLE: THE PRETENDER
ALBUM: ECHOES, SILENCE,
PATIENCE & GRACE
RELEASED: 2007
LABEL: RCA
GENRE: ROCK

PERSONNEL: DAVE GROHL (VOX+GTR)
TAYLOR HAWKINS (DRUMS)
NATE MENDEL (BASS)
CHRIS SHIFLET (GTR)

UK CHART PEAK: 8
US CHART PEAK: 37

BACKGROUND INFO

'The Pretender' was the first single released from the Foo Fighters' sixth studio album, *Echoes, Silence, Patience & Grace*.

THE BIGGER PICTURE

Not content with being a member of just one of rock's all-time great bands, Nirvana drummer Dave Grohl emerged from that outfit's tragic end in 1994 to rise again a year later with Foo Fighters, a project that began as a 100-copy demo. The Foo's signed to RCA and released these songs, which Grohl had played all the instruments on, as their eponymous debut. 'This Is A Call' proved a popular single, and the band's follow-up albums, 1997's *The Colour And The Shape* and 1999's *There Is Nothing Left To Lose*, ushered in various line-up changes and a more polished sound, yielding a reservoir of hits such as 'Everlong', 'Monkey Wrench', 'Learn To Fly' and 'My Hero'. 1995's double album *In Your Honor* comprised a hard-edged 'rock' half and a star-studded 'acoustic' half, whereas 2007's *Echoes, Silence, Patience & Grace* mixed the two sounds, and saw second-album producer Gil Norton return to the desk. Almost two decades on, the band's remarkable consistency has earned Foo Fighters their place in the pantheon of modern rock acts.

NOTES

'The Pretender' showcases what the Foo Fighters do best. An exercise in rock dynamics, it begins with a subdued, contemplative arpeggio intro before relentlessly upping the ante with layers of guitar and a chanted chorus, which Grohl admits may have been influenced by the *Sesame Street* song 'One Of These Things Is Not Like The Other'. Then the song takes a detour, swerving between a Chuck Berry-esque shuffle, the subdued intro and the all-out onslaught of the chorus – all in a breathless four and a half minutes. It was a relatively spontaneous creation, as Dave Grohl told *Guitar World*: "It was just something I fooled around with between takes… We put the whole thing together in five minutes. Then we recorded a demo version of it, and our demo version wound up being the basis of the recorded version. My guitars that we used on the demo are the ones on the final version."

RECOMMENDED LISTENING

The Colour And The Shape and *There Is Nothing Left To Lose* demonstrate Grohl's knack for crafting memorable melodic hooks, while 2011's *Wasted Light*, helmed by Nirvana producer Butch Vig, is a hard-hitting granite slab of rock.

The Pretender

Foo Fighters

Words & Music by Dave Grohl, Taylor Hawkins,
Nate Mendel & Chris Shiflett

Keep you_ in_ the_ dark._ You know they all_____ pre-tend.____

Keep you_ in_ the_ dark,_ and so_ it all_____ be-gan._____

Twice as fast

1. Send in___ your ske - le - tons.___

Sing as___their bones__ come march - ing in_____ a - gain.__

The need_ you bur - ied deep,

the se - crets that___ you keep_ are at_____ the rea - dy.

too late to a - pol - o - gize. It's too late.

I said, it's too late to a - pol - o - gize. It's

too late. **1.** I said, it's **2.** I'm

rall. hold - ing on your rope, got me ten feet off the ground.

A Song For You

Ray Charles
Words & Music by Leon Russell

Male Vocals Grade 8

Wait in the fire,_____ wait in the fire._____

To Coda ⊕   **D.C. al Coda** ⊕

Burn._____

⊕ *Coda*

Burn._____ Burn._____

Ah._____ Please._____

(2 & 3 *vocal ad lib.*)

1, 2.   ⌐ *2* ¬

Please._____

3.   **D.C. al Coda** ⊕⊕

leave_____ be - hind_____ ay ay.

⊕⊕ **Coda**

(1-4 *vocal ad lib.*)

(5-7) Wait in the fire,_____ wait in the fire._____

1-6.   **7.**

Grace

Livin' On A Prayer

Bon Jovi

Words & Music by Jon Bon Jovi, Richie Sambora & Desmond Child

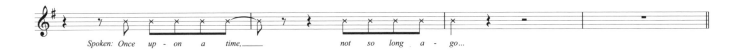

Spoken: Once up-on a time,____ not so long a-go...

1. Tom-my used to work on the docks.____ Un-ion's been on strike, he's down on his luck, it's
2. Tom-my's got his six string in hock.____ Now he's hold-ing in when he used to make it talk so

tough,____ so tough.____
tough,____ mm, it's tough.____

Gi-na works the din-er all day.____ Work-ing for her man, she brings home her pay____ for
Gi-na dreams of run-ning a-way.____ When she cries____ in the night, Tom-my whis-pers; "Ba-by, it's

love,____ mm, for love.____ She says: We've got to
o-kay,____ some-day."____ We got to

hold____ on____ to what we've got. It does-n't make a diff-'rence if we

Try A Little Tenderness

The Commitments

Words & Music by Harry Woods, James Campbell & Reginald Connelly

1. Oh, she may be wea - ry, and young girls, they do get wea - ry wear - ing that same old_____ shab - by dress._____ But when she gets wea - ry_____ try a lit - tle_____ ten - der - ness._____ (Fan - dan - go.)

2. You know she's wait - ing, just an - ti - ci - pat - ing_____ the things_____ that she nev - er, nev - er, nev - er, nev - er pos - ess - es, yeah.___ But while_____ she's there wait - ing with - out them, all you got - ta try_____ a lit - tle ten - der - ness.___ That's all you got - ta do.

3. You won't re - gret_____ it, young girls they nev - er for - get_____ it.___ Love_____ is their on - ly_____ hap - pi - ness. But it is all so eas - y, This is for you.

It's not just sen - ti - men - tal, no,_____ no.___

She has her grief_____ and_____ her care._____

But the soft words, _____ they are spoke _____ so _____ gen - tle, it makes it eas - - i - er,

D.S. al Coda

eas - i - er _____ to bear, _____ yeah. _____

Coda

do is try a lit - tle ten - der - ness.

Oh, yeah. _____ Squeeze her, we tease her, nev - er leave her. You got - ta, you got - ta, you got - ta, you got - ta try a lit - tle

ten - der - ness, yeah. _____ Yeah, _____ yeah.

Squeeze her, we tease her, nev - er leave _____ her. You got - ta, you got - ta, you got - ta,

Play 5 times ad lib

you got - ta try a lit - tle ten - der - ness. *(Vocal ad lib.)*

The Pretender

Foo Fighters

Words & Music by Dave Grohl, Taylor Hawkins,
Nate Mendel & Chris Shiflett

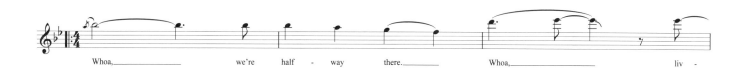

Grace

Jeff Buckley

Words & Music by Jeff Buckley & Gary Lucas

Apologize

OneRepublic

Words & Music by Ryan Tedder

Male Vocals Grade 8

SONG TITLE: LIVIN' ON A PRAYER
ALBUM: SLIPPERY WHEN WET
RELEASED: 1986
LABEL: MERCURY
GENRE: ROCK

PERSONNEL: JON BON JOVI (VOX)
RICHIE SAMBORA (GTR+VOX)
DAVID BRYAN (KEYS)
TICO TORRES (DRUMS)
ALEC JOHN SUCH (BASS)

UK CHART PEAK: 4
US CHART PEAK: 1

BACKGROUND INFO

'Livin' On A Prayer' was Bon Jovi's second US Number 1 from their third album, *Slippery When Wet*. It is credited to Jon Bon Jovi, Richie Sambora and producer/songwriter Desmond Child.

THE BIGGER PICTURE

Jon Bon Jovi himself didn't originally rate the nascent song, demo'd a year before, but Richie Sambora convinced him to continue work on it with a new bassline. It ended up being Bon Jovi's signature song. *Slippery When Wet* made the band superstars, the album having now sold a reported 28 million-plus copies. Its follow-up, *New Jersey*, was a double US/UK Number 1. At the 2010 Grammy Awards, Bon Jovi performed this song as a result of a fan vote. Asked the same year if he ever got tired of singing it, JBJ quipped, "Not when I see the jet with my name on it."

NOTES

This is a classic character song, about a fictional working-class couple, Tommy and Gina. Tommy "used to work on the docks" but then the "union's been on strike, he's down on his luck". Gina works at a diner, "workin' for her man". Jon Bon Jovi says the character Tommy went through changes: "It was a fictional character. The inspiration was a young couple who got pregnant and gave up everything they had, but that didn't read right, so we changed the story." Some have speculated the song is influenced by fellow New Jerseyan Bruce Springsteen, who used a similar scenario of hard economic times and a character couple in his 1981 song 'The River' – Springsteen is one of Jon Bon Jovi's songwriting heroes. However, Desmond Child says Tommy and Gina were based on people he knew while working as a New York City cab driver in the 1970s. The names? Jon Bon Jovi has family relations called Tommy and Gina. So it's a mix of inspirations.

RECOMMENDED LISTENING

The song works acoustically – see Bon Jovi and Sambora's performance at the 1989 MTV Music Awards. In 2000, on Bon Jovi's 'It's My Life,' Tommy and Gina returned as characters in song: "This is for the ones who stood their ground, for Tommy and Gina who never backed down." Sambora used a guitar talkbox on 'It's My Life' in a nod to the song's history. It's been in *Glee*, of course, and Bowling For Soup mentioned the characters in their 'Punk Rock 101' – "Like Tommy and Gina, they're living on a prayer."

Livin' On A Prayer

Bon Jovi

Words & Music by Jon Bon Jovi, Richie Sambora & Desmond Child

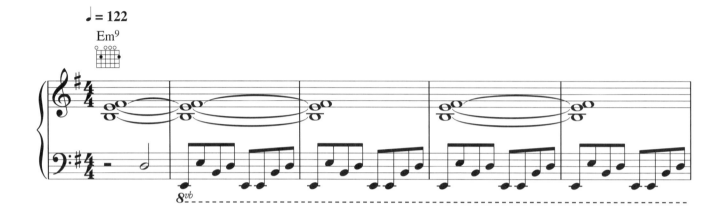

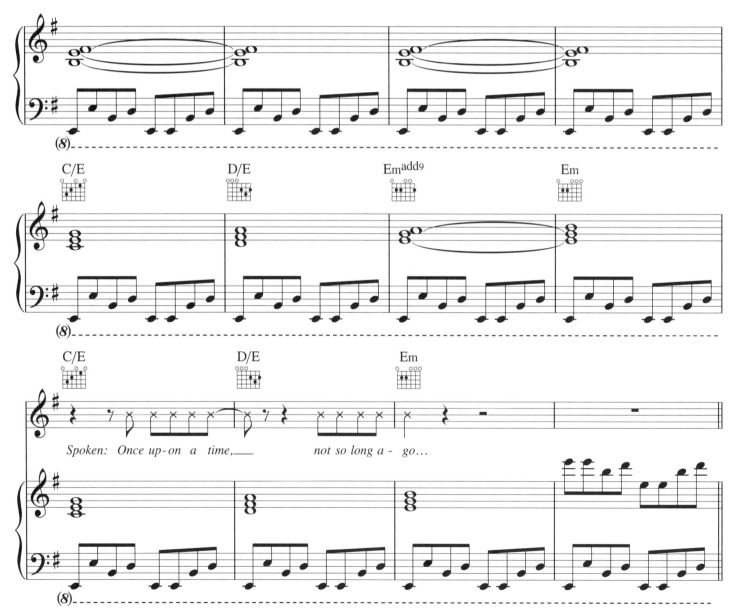

Spoken: Once up-on a time,___ not so long a - go...

1. Tom - my used to work on the docks.___
2. Tom - my's got his six string in hock.___ Now

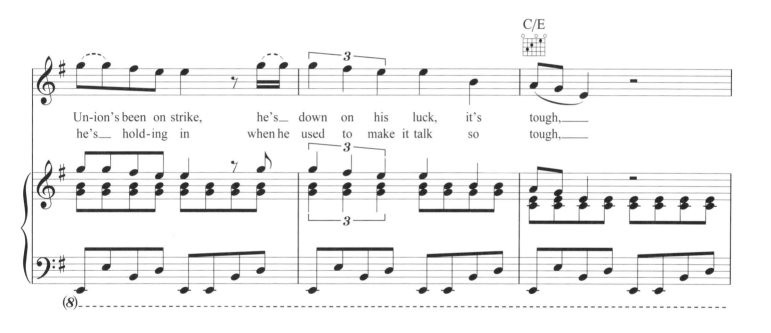

Un-ion's been on strike, he's__ down on his luck, it's tough,___
he's__ hold-ing in when he used to make it talk so tough,___

C/E

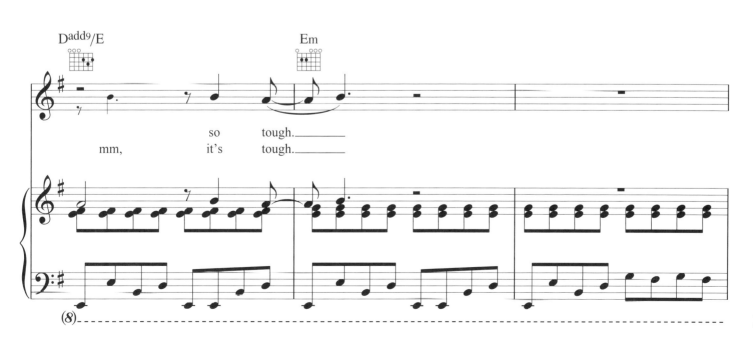

D^{add9}/E

Em

so tough.___
mm, it's tough.___

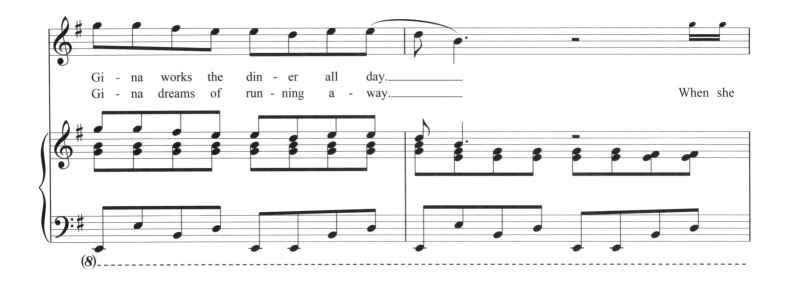

Gi - na works the din - er all day._____
Gi - na dreams of run - ning a - way._____

When she

C/E

Work-ing for her man,   she brings home her pay___ for   love,_____
cries___ in the night,   Tom-my whis - pers;   "Ba - by, it's   o - kay,_____

Dadd9/E   Em

mm,   for   love._____   She says: We've got to⎞
some - day."_____   We got to⎠

SONG TITLE: TRY A LITTLE TENDERNESS
ALBUM: THE COMMITMENTS
RELEASED: 1991
LABEL: MCA
GENRE: SOUL

PERSONNEL: ANDREW STRONG (VOX)
MARIA DOYLE KENNEDY (VOX)
BRONAGH GALLAGHER (VOX)
ANGELINE BALL (VOX)
MICHAEL AHERNE (KEYS)
GLEN HANSARD (GUITAR)
KEN MCCLUSKEY (BASS)
DICK MASSEY (DRUMS)
FÉLIM GORMLEY (SAX)

UK CHART PEAK: N/A
US CHART PEAK: N/A

BACKGROUND INFO

'Try A Little Tenderness' was one of the standout recordings from the 1991 film *The Commitments*. It is a cover of Otis Redding's 1966 version of a song written in 1932.

THE BIGGER PICTURE

The Commitments was a film adaptation of the novel of the same name by acclaimed Irish writer Roddy Doyle (whose other novel *Paddy Clarke Ha Ha Ha* won the Booker Prize in 1993). The film is set in Dublin and tells the story of a soul band made up of white working class Dubliners. Alan Parker, the film's director, picked real musicians to play the fictional band members, preferring musical ability over acting chops. This resulted in an authenticity to the film's musical performances and most of the cast being featured on the accompanying soundtrack album, released in the same year as the movie. The soundtrack features a number of classic songs from labels such as Motown, Atlantic and Stax. 'Try A Little Tenderness' is a key song in the development of the band as it is depicted in the film, and was based on Otis Redding's version for Stax Records.

NOTES

Written in 1932 by Woods, Campbell and Connelly, 'Try A Little Tenderness' had been performed by everyone from Bing Crosby to Aretha Franklin. Cut in three takes in 1966, Otis Redding's version begins with a three-part horn intro, leading into a sparse showcase of his restrained yet emotional vocal. Three minutes and 46 seconds after it began, Redding and the band had one of pop's greatest ensemble performances in the can. Quoted in Robert Gordon's *Respect Yourself*, Stax Records co-founder Jim Stewart considered it the label's best record: "It exemplifies what Stax really was, that one record. When I hear it today, I still get that same feeling that I got when we rolled that tape in the studio." For the young, unknown cast of *The Commitments* to replicate that as well as they did was no mean feat.

RECOMMENDED LISTENING

The Commitments soundtrack album (1991) is an impressive achievement by the film's youthful cast. Otis Redding's third solo album, *Otis Blue* (1966), is essential and the posthumous *Dock Of The Bay* (1968) is a fitting tribute.

Try A Little Tenderness

The Commitments

Words & Music by Harry Woods, James Campbell & Reginald Connelly

1. Oh, she may be wea-ry, and young girls, they do get wea-ry wear-ing that same old_____ shab-by dress._____

But when she gets wea - ry_____ try

a lit - tle_____ ten - der - ness._____

(Fan - dan - go.)

2. You
3. You

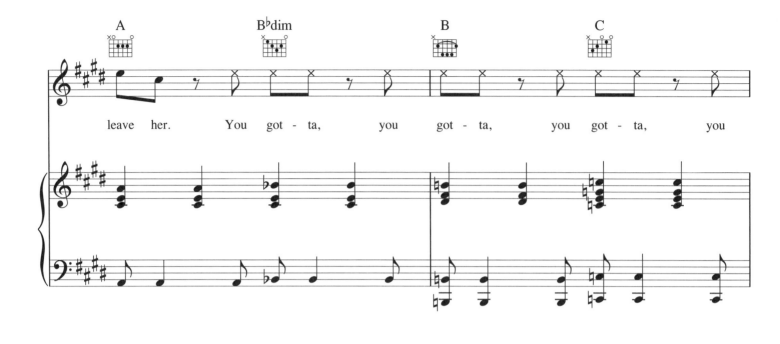

leave her. You got - ta, you got - ta, you got - ta, you

got - ta try a lit - tle ten - der - ness, yeah.___

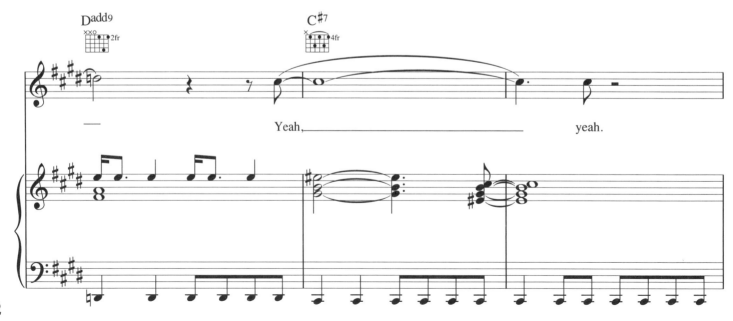

___ Yeah,_____ yeah.

Squeeze her, we tease her, nev - er leave_____ her. You gotta,

Play 5 times ad lib

you got - ta, you got - ta, you got - ta try a lit - tle

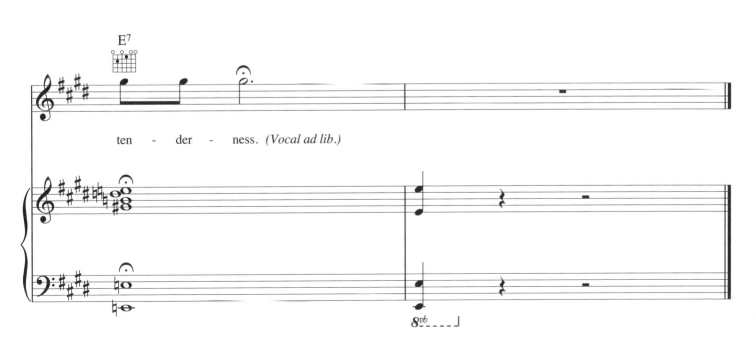

ten - der - ness. *(Vocal ad lib.)*

Technical Exercises

Group A: Scales

The chromatic scale should be prepared as shown below. You may select any starting note from A–E. You will be asked if you would like to sing along to a metronome click or hear four clicks before you start. Whichever option you choose, you will hear your chosen starting note before the count starts. You may perform this test using any vocal sound except humming or whistling. The tempo is ♩=100.

Group B: Arpeggios

In this group, the arpeggio exercise needs to be prepared as shown below.

This test is performed to a metronome click track and you may select any starting note from C–G. You will hear the root note played on piano followed by a one-bar (four click) count-in. You may perform this test using any vocal sound except humming or whistling. The tempo is ♩=100.

C diminished⁷ arpeggio

Group C: Intervals

In this group, the two interval sequences need to be prepared as below. You will be asked to perform one of them in the exam, as chosen by the examiner.

The examiner will choose a starting note within the range D–F. You will hear this note followed by a four-beat count-in. You may perform this test using any vocal sound except humming or whistling. The tempo is ♩=90.

Major 7th, minor 7th and octave intervals

Major 3rd and minor 3rd intervals

Group D: Backing Vocals

In this group, all three backing vocal parts need to be prepared as shown below. You will be asked to perform one of them in the exam, as chosen by the examiner. The chosen part must be sung alongside the other two parts on the recording. The backing tracks for these can be found on the download card.

Group E: Stylistic Studies

You will need to choose *one* stylistic technical study from the group listed below. Your choice will determine the style of the Quick Study Piece. If you choose the jazz and blues stylistic study, for example, the examiner will give you a QSP from the jazz and blues group.

- Pop and musical theatre
- Soul and R'n'B
- Jazz and blues
- Rock and indie

Stylistic Study | Pop and Musical Theatre

Dramatic dynamics and inflections / Sustains with vibrato

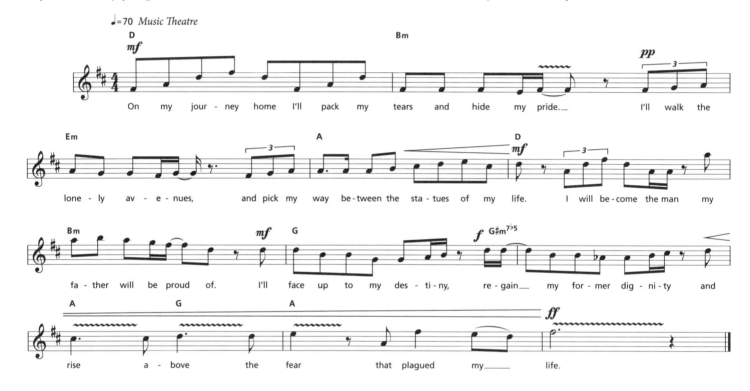

Stylistic Study | Soul and R'n'B

Long melisma / Register flips

Stylistic Study | Jazz and Blues

Un-accompanied chromatic runs / Wide pitch jumps

Stylistic Study | Rock and Indie

Slides to scream / Register flips

Quick Study Piece

At this grade you will be asked to prepare and perform a short Quick Study Piece (QSP). This will consist of four bars of melody and eight bars of improvisation. Bars 1–4 of the test will be a notated melody and you will need to sing all the written detail, including lyrics. In bars 5–8, you will need to improvise a variation on bars 1–4, developing both the lyrics and melody as you feel appropriate. In bars 9–12, you will need to improvise with no requirement to reference bars 1–4. You may use any vocal sound except humming or whistling for these bars.

The examiner will give you the sheet music, then you will hear a full mix version of the track, including the notated parts. This first playthrough will be preceded by the root note and a one-bar count-in. After the full mix, you will have three minutes to practise. The root note will be played at the start of this practice time and then again after 90 seconds. During the practice time, you will be given the choice of a metronome click throughout or a one-bar count-in at the beginning.

At the end of three minutes, the backing track will be played twice more with the notated parts now absent. The first time is for you to rehearse and the second time is for you to perform the final version for the exam. Again, you will hear the root note and a one-bar count-in before both playthroughs. The backing track is continuous, so once the first playthrough has finished, the root note and count-in of the second playthrough will start immediately. The tempo is ♩=70–160.

The QSP style will be from one of the following four groups. These match the groups of the stylistic studies in the Technical Exercises section.

- Pop and musical theatre
- Soul and R'n'B
- Jazz and blues
- Rock and indie

The style given to you in the exam will be from the same group as your choice of stylistic study. The examiner will decide which one, specifically (i.e. rock *or* indie).

Quick Study Piece | Pop and Musical Theatre   *Example test*

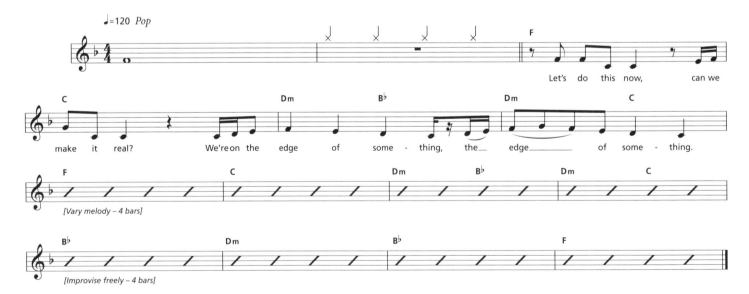

Quick Study Piece | Soul and R'n'B

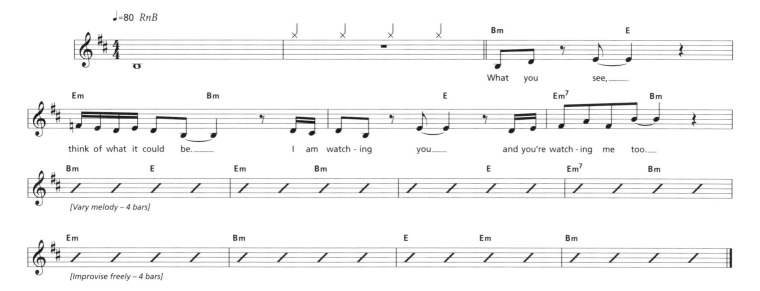

Quick Study Piece | Jazz and Blues

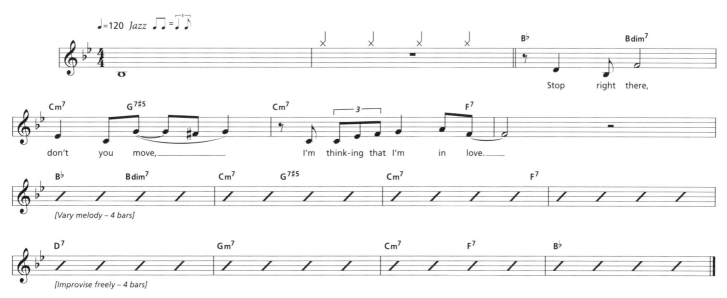

Quick Study Piece | Rock and Indie

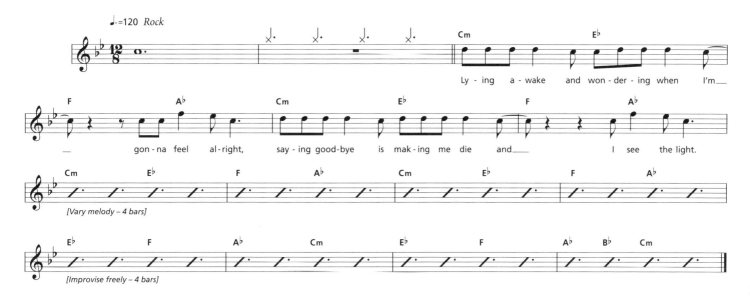

Ear Tests

In this section, there are two ear tests:
- Melodic Recall
- Harmony Vocals

You will find one example of each type of test printed below and you will be given both of them in the exam.

Test 1 | Melodic Recall

The examiner will play you a two-bar melody played to a drum backing. It will use the D major or E natural minor scale (the examiner will decide which) and the first note will be the root, 3rd or 5th. You will hear the test twice. Each time the test is played, it starts with the root note and a four-beat count-in. There will be a short gap for you to practise after each playthrough. Next you will hear a *vocal* count-in, after which you should sing the melody to the drum backing. The tempo is ♩=90.

It is acceptable to sing over the track as it is being played as well as practising after the first two playthroughs. The length of time available after the second playthrough is pre-recorded on the audio track, so the vocal count-in may begin while you are still practising.

You may perform this test using any vocal sound except humming or whistling.

Please note: the test shown is an example. The examiner will give you a different version in the exam.

Test 2 | Harmony Vocals

The examiner will play you a four-bar melody in the key of D major or E minor, based on any diatonic chords. There will be two recorded vocal parts that will sing the root, 3rd or 5th of each chord, and you need to harmonise a diatonic 3rd or 4th above the highest-sounding part using the same rhythm. The examiner will give you the lyrics.

You will hear the test twice. Each time the test is played, it starts with the root note and a four-beat count-in. There will be a short gap for you to practise after each playthrough. Next, you will hear a *vocal* count-in, after which you should perform the harmony line. The tempo is ♩=90–140.

It is acceptable to sing over the track as it is being played as well as practising after the first two playthroughs. The length of time available after the second playthrough is pre-recorded on the audio track, so the vocal count-in may begin while you are still practising.

Please note: the test shown is an example. The examiner will give you a different version in the exam.

General Musicianship Questions

In this part of the exam you will be asked five questions. Three of these will be about general music knowledge, the fourth will be about improvisation, and the fifth will be about your voice or the microphone.

Part 1 | General Music Knowledge

The examiner will ask three music knowledge questions from the categories below. The questions will be based on one of the pieces (including Free Choice Pieces) as performed by you in the exam. You can choose which one.

If there are handwritten notes on the piece you have chosen, the examiner may ask you to choose an alternative.

You will be asked to *identify and explain:*
- Any notation used in the chosen piece;
- Recognition of intervals up to a 10th between two adjacent notes. (You will need to state major, minor or perfect.)

Part 2 | Improvisation

You will also be asked to briefly *describe and demonstrate* – with reference to melody, rhythm, phrasing and dynamics – your approach to how you would improvise any part of your chosen song. You can choose the part.

Part 3 | Your Voice And The Microphone

The examiner will also ask you one question about your voice or the microphone. Brief demonstrations to assist your answer would be acceptable.

You will be asked:
- What is 'melisma' and what exercises can help you develop it?
- Describe techniques you might employ to build emotional intensity in a soul/R'n'B-style ballad.
- Give two examples of exercises designed to develop intensity/power in a singer's 'mix' voice.
- Explain the difference between a dynamic and a condenser microphone, including one example each of their uses.

Entering Exams, Exam Procedure & Marking Schemes

Entering Exams

Entering a Rockschool exam is easy. You can enter online at *www.rockschool.co.uk* or by downloading and filling in an exam entry form. The full Rockschool examination terms and conditions as well as exam periods and current fees are available from our website or by calling +44 (0)845 460 4747.

Exam procedure

In the exam you can decide whether to start with the Performance Pieces or the Technical Exercises. These will be followed by the Supporting Tests (Ear Tests and Quick Study Pieces) and General Musicianship Questions.

Use Of Microphone

At Level 1 (Grades 1–3) microphone use is optional, although candidates may use one if they feel it will enhance their performance. At Level 2 (Grades 4–5) microphone use is obligatory for all pieces and at Level 3 (Grades 6–8) for the whole exam.

Marking Schemes

Below are the marking schemes for the two different types of Rockschool exam.

GRADE EXAMS | GRADES 6–8

ELEMENT	PASS	MERIT	DISTINCTION
Performance Piece 1	12–14 out of 20	15–17 out of 20	18+ out of 20
Performance Piece 2	12–14 out of 20	15–17 out of 20	18+ out of 20
Performance Piece 3	12–14 out of 20	15–17 out of 20	18+ out of 20
Technical Exercises	9–10 out of 15	11–12 out of 15	13+ out of 15
Quick Study Piece	6 out of 10	7–8 out of 10	9+ out of 10
Ear Tests	6 out of 10	7–8 out of 10	9+ out of 10
General Musicianship Questions	3 out of 5	4 out of 5	5 out of 5
TOTAL MARKS	60%+	74%+	90%+

PERFORMANCE CERTIFICATES | GRADES 1–8

ELEMENT	PASS	MERIT	DISTINCTION
Performance Piece 1	12–14 out of 20	15–17 out of 20	18+ out of 20
Performance Piece 2	12–14 out of 20	15–17 out of 20	18+ out of 20
Performance Piece 3	12–14 out of 20	15–17 out of 20	18+ out of 20
Performance Piece 4	12–14 out of 20	15–17 out of 20	18+ out of 20
Performance Piece 5	12–14 out of 20	15–17 out of 20	18+ out of 20
TOTAL MARKS	60%+	75%+	90%+